PEANUTS Every Sunday

PEANUTS®
Every Sunday

By CHARLES M. SCHULZ

A PEANUTS® BOOK

HOLT, RINEHART AND WINSTON
New York / Chicago / San Francisco

First published in book form, April, 1961

Library of Congress Catalog Card Number: 61-7132

This edition published by Mattel Home Programs, Inc., by
arrangement with Holt, Rinehart and Winston, Inc.

Printed in the United States of America

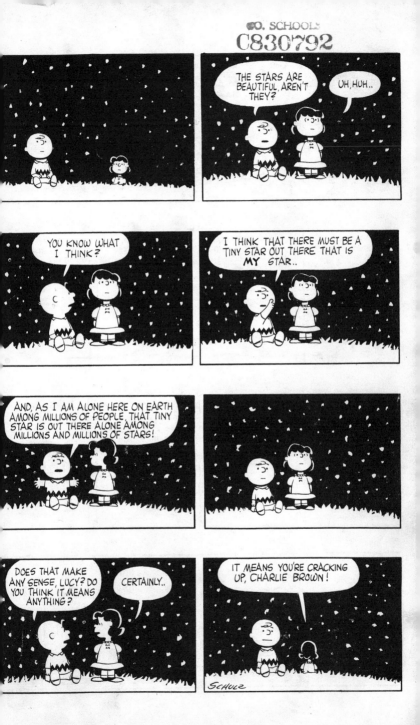

DEAR PENCIL-PAL,
I GUESS BY THIS TIME EVERYBODY BUT YOU KNOWS THAT I HAVE A BABY SISTER.

I SHOULD HAVE WRITTEN SOONER TO TELL YOU, BUT I HAVE BEEN VERY BUSY. HER NAME IS SALLY. WE LIKE HER AND SHE LIKES US.

OH, OH!

IN A WAY, THIS HAS BEEN A GOOD EXPERIENCE FOR ME. I HAVE LEARNED A LOT.
AS EVER,
CHARLIE BROWN

SCHULZ

CLOMP

YOU KNOW, I CAN'T POSSIBLY TELL YOU HOW SICK I GET OF SEEING YOU DRAG AROUND THAT STUPID BLANKET!

IT'S NOT STUPID... THIS BLANKET HAS MANY VERY PRACTICAL USES...

HA! THAT'S A LAUGH!

YOU JUST HAVE NO IMAGINATION, THAT'S ALL

I HAVE PLENTY IMAGINATION... IT DOESN'T TAKE ANY IMAGINATION TO SEE HE'S **CRAZY!**

OF ALL THE BROTHERS IN THE WORLD, I HAD TO GET **HIM!**

WELL, YOU'LL HAVE TO ADMIT HE'S DONE IT AGAIN!

HUH?

I SAID LINUS HAS DONE IT AGAIN..YOU'D BETTER GO SEE FOR YOURSELF...

SCHULZ

WELL, HOW DID THE SKIING GO?

I CAN TAKE IT OR LEAVE IT!

THUS ENDETH THE CROQUET GAME!

SCHULZ